TWIN

mama ♥ ♥

Baby Feeding and Diaper Log

Record over 3 months worth of your twins' feedings, diapers, medicine, and activities.

Created by a twin mom for twin moms.

Scrappin' Twins

www.scrappintwins.com

Twin Baby Log

Time	Feeding	Diaper	Medicine	Feeding	Diaper	Medicine

Tummy Time

	◯ ◯ ◯ ◯ ◯
	◯ ◯ ◯ ◯ ◯

To Do

Activities

Time		

Notes

Twin Baby Log

Time	Feeding	Diaper	Medicine	Feeding	Diaper	Medicine

Tummy Time

○ ○ ○ ○ ○
○ ○ ○ ○ ○

To Do

Activities

Time		

Notes

Twin Baby Log

Time	Feeding	Diaper	Medicine	Feeding	Diaper	Medicine

Tummy Time

	○ ○ ○ ○ ○
	○ ○ ○ ○ ○

To Do

Activities

Time		

Notes

Twin Baby Log

Time	Feeding	Diaper	Medicine	Feeding	Diaper	Medicine

Tummy Time

	○ ○ ○ ○ ○
	○ ○ ○ ○ ○

To Do

Activities

Time		

Notes

Twin Baby Log

Time	Feeding	Diaper	Medicine	Feeding	Diaper	Medicine

Tummy Time

	○ ○ ○ ○ ○
	○ ○ ○ ○ ○

To Do

Activities

Time		

Notes

Twin Baby Log

Time	Feeding	Diaper	Medicine	Feeding	Diaper	Medicine

Tummy Time

	○ ○ ○ ○ ○
	○ ○ ○ ○ ○

To Do

Activities

Time		

Notes

Twin Baby Log

Time	Feeding	Diaper	Medicine	Feeding	Diaper	Medicine

Tummy Time	To Do
○ ○ ○ ○ ○	
○ ○ ○ ○ ○	

Activities			Notes
Time			

Twin Baby Log

Time	Feeding	Diaper	Medicine	Feeding	Diaper	Medicine

Tummy Time

	◯ ◯ ◯ ◯ ◯
	◯ ◯ ◯ ◯ ◯

To Do

Activities

Time		

Notes

Twin Baby Log

Time	Feeding	Diaper	Medicine	Feeding	Diaper	Medicine

Tummy Time

	◯ ◯ ◯ ◯ ◯
	◯ ◯ ◯ ◯ ◯

To Do

Activities

Time		

Notes

Twin Baby Log

Time	Feeding	Diaper	Medicine	Feeding	Diaper	Medicine

Tummy Time

	○ ○ ○ ○ ○
	○ ○ ○ ○ ○

To Do

Activities

Time		

Notes

Twin Baby Log

Time	Feeding	Diaper	Medicine	Feeding	Diaper	Medicine

Tummy Time

○ ○ ○ ○ ○
○ ○ ○ ○ ○

To Do

Activities

Time		

Notes

Twin Baby Log

Time	Feeding	Diaper	Medicine	Feeding	Diaper	Medicine

Tummy Time	
	○ ○ ○ ○ ○
	○ ○ ○ ○ ○

To Do

Activities		
Time		

Notes

DATE: _____

M TU W TH F SA SU

Twin Baby Log

Time	Feeding	Diaper	Medicine	Feeding	Diaper	Medicine

Tummy Time		To Do
	○○○○○	
	○○○○○	

Activities

Time		

Notes

Twin Baby Log

Time	Feeding	Diaper	Medicine	Feeding	Diaper	Medicine

Tummy Time

| | ◯ ◯ ◯ ◯ ◯ |
| | ◯ ◯ ◯ ◯ ◯ |

To Do

Activities

Time		

Notes

DATE: _____

M TU W TH F SA SU

Twin Baby Log

Time	Feeding	Diaper	Medicine	Feeding	Diaper	Medicine

Tummy Time

	◯ ◯ ◯ ◯ ◯
	◯ ◯ ◯ ◯ ◯

To Do

Activities

Time		

Notes

Twin Baby Log

Time		Feeding	Diaper	Medicine	Feeding	Diaper	Medicine

Tummy Time

	○ ○ ○ ○ ○
	○ ○ ○ ○ ○

To Do

Activities

Time		

Notes

Twin Baby Log

Time	Feeding	Diaper	Medicine	Feeding	Diaper	Medicine

Tummy Time

| | ◯ ◯ ◯ ◯ ◯ |
| | ◯ ◯ ◯ ◯ ◯ |

To Do

Activities

Time		

Notes

Twin Baby Log

Time		Feeding	Diaper	Medicine	Feeding	Diaper	Medicine

Tummy Time

	○ ○ ○ ○ ○
	○ ○ ○ ○ ○

To Do

Activities

Time		

Notes

Twin Baby Log

Time	Feeding	Diaper	Medicine	Feeding	Diaper	Medicine

Tummy Time

	○ ○ ○ ○ ○
	○ ○ ○ ○ ○

To Do

Activities

Time		

Notes

Twin Baby Log

DATE: _____

M TU W TH F SA SU

Time		Feeding	Diaper	Medicine	Feeding	Diaper	Medicine

Tummy Time

	○ ○ ○ ○ ○
	○ ○ ○ ○ ○

To Do

Activities

Time		

Notes

Twin Baby Log

Time	Feeding	Diaper	Medicine	Feeding	Diaper	Medicine

Tummy Time

○ ○ ○ ○ ○
○ ○ ○ ○ ○

To Do

Activities

Time		

Notes

Twin Baby Log

Time	Feeding	Diaper	Medicine	Feeding	Diaper	Medicine

Tummy Time
○ ○ ○ ○ ○
○ ○ ○ ○ ○

To Do

Activities		
Time		

Notes

Twin Baby Log

Time	Feeding	Diaper	Medicine	Feeding	Diaper	Medicine

Tummy Time

| | ◯ ◯ ◯ ◯ ◯ |
| | ◯ ◯ ◯ ◯ ◯ |

To Do

Activities

Time		

Notes

Twin Baby Log

Time	Feeding	Diaper	Medicine	Feeding	Diaper	Medicine

Tummy Time

	○ ○ ○ ○ ○
	○ ○ ○ ○ ○

To Do

Activities

Time		

Notes

Twin Baby Log

Time	Feeding	Diaper	Medicine	Feeding	Diaper	Medicine

Tummy Time

	○ ○ ○ ○ ○
	○ ○ ○ ○ ○

To Do

Activities

Time		

Notes

Twin Baby Log

Time	Feeding	Diaper	Medicine	Feeding	Diaper	Medicine

Tummy Time

◯ ◯ ◯ ◯ ◯
◯ ◯ ◯ ◯ ◯

To Do

Activities

Time		

Notes

Twin Baby Log

Time	Feeding	Diaper	Medicine	Feeding	Diaper	Medicine

Tummy Time

	○ ○ ○ ○ ○
	○ ○ ○ ○ ○

To Do

Activities

Time		

Notes

Twin Baby Log

Time	Feeding	Diaper	Medicine	Feeding	Diaper	Medicine

Tummy Time

| ○ ○ ○ ○ ○ |
| ○ ○ ○ ○ ○ |

To Do

Activities

Time		

Notes

Twin Baby Log

Time	Feeding	Diaper	Medicine	Feeding	Diaper	Medicine

Tummy Time

	○ ○ ○ ○ ○
	○ ○ ○ ○ ○

To Do

Activities

Time		

Notes

Twin Baby Log

Time	Feeding	Diaper	Medicine	Feeding	Diaper	Medicine

Tummy Time

	◯ ◯ ◯ ◯ ◯
	◯ ◯ ◯ ◯ ◯

To Do

Activities

Time		

Notes

Twin Baby Log

Time	Feeding	Diaper	Medicine	Feeding	Diaper	Medicine

Tummy Time

	○ ○ ○ ○ ○
	○ ○ ○ ○ ○

To Do

Activities

Time		

Notes

Twin Baby Log

Time		Feeding	Diaper	Medicine	Feeding	Diaper	Medicine

Tummy Time

	○ ○ ○ ○ ○
	○ ○ ○ ○ ○

To Do

Activities

Time		

Notes

Twin Baby Log

Time	Feeding	Diaper	Medicine	Feeding	Diaper	Medicine

Tummy Time

◯ ◯ ◯ ◯ ◯
◯ ◯ ◯ ◯ ◯

To Do

Activities

Time		

Notes

Twin Baby Log

Time	Feeding	Diaper	Medicine	Feeding	Diaper	Medicine

Tummy Time

	◯ ◯ ◯ ◯ ◯
	◯ ◯ ◯ ◯ ◯

To Do

Activities

Time		

Notes

Twin Baby Log

Time	Feeding	Diaper	Medicine	Feeding	Diaper	Medicine

Tummy Time

	○ ○ ○ ○ ○
	○ ○ ○ ○ ○

To Do

Activities

Time		

Notes

Twin Baby Log

Time		Feeding	Diaper	Medicine	Feeding	Diaper	Medicine

Tummy Time	
	⚪⚪⚪⚪⚪
	⚪⚪⚪⚪⚪

To Do

Activities		
Time		

Notes

Twin Baby Log

Time	Feeding	Diaper	Medicine	Feeding	Diaper	Medicine

Tummy Time

	○ ○ ○ ○ ○
	○ ○ ○ ○ ○

To Do

Activities

Time		

Notes

Twin Baby Log

Time	Feeding	Diaper	Medicine	Feeding	Diaper	Medicine

Tummy Time

	○ ○ ○ ○ ○
	○ ○ ○ ○ ○

To Do

Activities

Time		

Notes

Twin Baby Log

Time	Feeding	Diaper	Medicine	Feeding	Diaper	Medicine

Tummy Time

	◯ ◯ ◯ ◯ ◯
	◯ ◯ ◯ ◯ ◯

To Do

Activities

Time		

Notes

Twin Baby Log

Time	Feeding	Diaper	Medicine	Feeding	Diaper	Medicine

Tummy Time

	◯ ◯ ◯ ◯ ◯
	◯ ◯ ◯ ◯ ◯

To Do

Activities

Time		

Notes

Twin Baby Log

Time	Feeding	Diaper	Medicine	Feeding	Diaper	Medicine

Tummy Time

	○ ○ ○ ○ ○
	○ ○ ○ ○ ○

To Do

Activities

Time		

Notes

Twin Baby Log

Time	Feeding	Diaper	Medicine	Feeding	Diaper	Medicine

Tummy Time

	○ ○ ○ ○ ○
	○ ○ ○ ○ ○

To Do

Activities

Time		

Notes

Twin Baby Log

Time	Feeding	Diaper	Medicine	Feeding	Diaper	Medicine

Tummy Time		To Do
	○○○○○	
	○○○○○	

Activities			Notes
Time			

Twin Baby Log

Time	Feeding	Diaper	Medicine	Feeding	Diaper	Medicine

Tummy Time

	◯ ◯ ◯ ◯ ◯
	◯ ◯ ◯ ◯ ◯

To Do

Activities

Time		

Notes

Twin Baby Log

Time	Feeding	Diaper	Medicine	Feeding	Diaper	Medicine

Tummy Time

	○ ○ ○ ○ ○
	○ ○ ○ ○ ○

To Do

| |
| |

Activities

Time		

Notes

| |
| |
| |
| |
| |
| |
| |
| |
| |
| |

Twin Baby Log

Time	Feeding	Diaper	Medicine	Feeding	Diaper	Medicine

Tummy Time

	○ ○ ○ ○ ○
	○ ○ ○ ○ ○

To Do

Activities

Time		

Notes

Twin Baby Log

Time	Feeding	Diaper	Medicine	Feeding	Diaper	Medicine

Tummy Time
○ ○ ○ ○ ○
○ ○ ○ ○ ○

To Do

Activities		
Time		

Notes

Twin Baby Log

Time	Feeding	Diaper	Medicine	Feeding	Diaper	Medicine

Tummy Time

	○ ○ ○ ○ ○
	○ ○ ○ ○ ○

To Do

Activities

Time		

Notes

Twin Baby Log

Time	Feeding	Diaper	Medicine	Feeding	Diaper	Medicine

Tummy Time

	○ ○ ○ ○ ○
	○ ○ ○ ○ ○

To Do

Activities

Time		

Notes

Twin Baby Log

Time	Feeding	Diaper	Medicine	Feeding	Diaper	Medicine

Tummy Time

	○ ○ ○ ○ ○
	○ ○ ○ ○ ○

To Do

Activities

Time		

Notes

Twin Baby Log

Time	Feeding	Diaper	Medicine	Feeding	Diaper	Medicine

Tummy Time

	○ ○ ○ ○ ○
	○ ○ ○ ○ ○

To Do

Activities

Time		

Notes

Twin Baby Log

Time	Feeding	Diaper	Medicine	Feeding	Diaper	Medicine

Tummy Time

	◯ ◯ ◯ ◯ ◯
	◯ ◯ ◯ ◯ ◯

To Do

Activities

Time		

Notes

Twin Baby Log

Time		Feeding	Diaper	Medicine	Feeding	Diaper	Medicine

Tummy Time

◯ ◯ ◯ ◯ ◯
◯ ◯ ◯ ◯ ◯

To Do

Activities

Time		

Notes

Twin Baby Log

Time	Feeding	Diaper	Medicine	Feeding	Diaper	Medicine

Tummy Time

	◯ ◯ ◯ ◯ ◯
	◯ ◯ ◯ ◯ ◯

To Do

Activities

Time		

Notes

Twin Baby Log

Time	Feeding	Diaper	Medicine	Feeding	Diaper	Medicine

Tummy Time	
	○○○○○
	○○○○○

To Do

Activities		
Time		

Notes

Twin Baby Log

Time	Feeding	Diaper	Medicine	Feeding	Diaper	Medicine

Tummy Time

◯ ◯ ◯ ◯ ◯
◯ ◯ ◯ ◯ ◯

To Do

Activities

Time		

Notes

Twin Baby Log

Time	Feeding	Diaper	Medicine	Feeding	Diaper	Medicine

Tummy Time		To Do
	○ ○ ○ ○ ○	
	○ ○ ○ ○ ○	

Activities

Time		

Notes

Twin Baby Log

Time	Feeding	Diaper	Medicine	Feeding	Diaper	Medicine

Tummy Time

	○ ○ ○ ○ ○
	○ ○ ○ ○ ○

To Do

Activities

Time		

Notes

Twin Baby Log

Time	Feeding	Diaper	Medicine	Feeding	Diaper	Medicine

Tummy Time

	⃝ ⃝ ⃝ ⃝ ⃝
	⃝ ⃝ ⃝ ⃝ ⃝

To Do

Activities

Time		

Notes

Twin Baby Log

Time	Feeding	Diaper	Medicine	Feeding	Diaper	Medicine

Tummy Time

	◯ ◯ ◯ ◯ ◯
	◯ ◯ ◯ ◯ ◯

To Do

Activities

Time		

Notes

Twin Baby Log

Time	Feeding	Diaper	Medicine	Feeding	Diaper	Medicine

Tummy Time

	◯ ◯ ◯ ◯ ◯
	◯ ◯ ◯ ◯ ◯

To Do

Activities

Time		

Notes

Twin Baby Log

Time	Feeding	Diaper	Medicine	Feeding	Diaper	Medicine

Tummy Time	To Do
○ ○ ○ ○ ○	
○ ○ ○ ○ ○	

Activities			Notes
Time			

Twin Baby Log

Time	Feeding	Diaper	Medicine	Feeding	Diaper	Medicine

Tummy Time

	◯ ◯ ◯ ◯ ◯
	◯ ◯ ◯ ◯ ◯

To Do

Activities

Time		

Notes

DATE: _____

M TU W TH F SA SU

Twin Baby Log

Time	Feeding	Diaper	Medicine	Feeding	Diaper	Medicine

Tummy Time

	○ ○ ○ ○ ○
	○ ○ ○ ○ ○

To Do

Activities

Time		

Notes

Twin Baby Log

DATE: _____

Time	Feeding	Diaper	Medicine	Feeding	Diaper	Medicine

Tummy Time

	○ ○ ○ ○ ○
	○ ○ ○ ○ ○

To Do

Activities

Time		

Notes

Twin Baby Log

Time	Feeding	Diaper	Medicine	Feeding	Diaper	Medicine

Tummy Time

	○ ○ ○ ○ ○
	○ ○ ○ ○ ○

To Do

Activities

Time		

Notes

Twin Baby Log

DATE: _____

Time	Feeding	Diaper	Medicine	Feeding	Diaper	Medicine

Tummy Time

	◯ ◯ ◯ ◯ ◯
	◯ ◯ ◯ ◯ ◯

To Do

Activities

Time		

Notes

Twin Baby Log

Time	Feeding	Diaper	Medicine	Feeding	Diaper	Medicine

Tummy Time

	○ ○ ○ ○ ○
	○ ○ ○ ○ ○

To Do

Activities

Time		

Notes

Twin Baby Log

Time	Feeding	Diaper	Medicine	Feeding	Diaper	Medicine

Tummy Time

	◯ ◯ ◯ ◯ ◯
	◯ ◯ ◯ ◯ ◯

To Do

Activities

Time		

Notes

Twin Baby Log

Time	Feeding	Diaper	Medicine	Feeding	Diaper	Medicine

Tummy Time

	○ ○ ○ ○ ○
	○ ○ ○ ○ ○

To Do

Activities

Time		

Notes

Twin Baby Log

Time	Feeding	Diaper	Medicine	Feeding	Diaper	Medicine

Tummy Time

◯ ◯ ◯ ◯ ◯
◯ ◯ ◯ ◯ ◯

To Do

Activities

Time		

Notes

Twin Baby Log

Time	Feeding	Diaper	Medicine	Feeding	Diaper	Medicine

Tummy Time

	○ ○ ○ ○ ○
	○ ○ ○ ○ ○

To Do

Activities

Time		

Notes

Twin Baby Log

Time	Feeding	Diaper	Medicine	Feeding	Diaper	Medicine

Tummy Time

○ ○ ○ ○ ○
○ ○ ○ ○ ○

To Do

Activities

Time		

Notes

Twin Baby Log

Time	Feeding	Diaper	Medicine	Feeding	Diaper	Medicine

Tummy Time

◯ ◯ ◯ ◯ ◯
◯ ◯ ◯ ◯ ◯

To Do

Activities

Time		

Notes

Twin Baby Log

Time	Feeding	Diaper	Medicine	Feeding	Diaper	Medicine

Tummy Time	
	◯ ◯ ◯ ◯ ◯
	◯ ◯ ◯ ◯ ◯

To Do

Activities		
Time		

Notes

Twin Baby Log

Time	Feeding	Diaper	Medicine	Feeding	Diaper	Medicine

Tummy Time

	◯ ◯ ◯ ◯ ◯
	◯ ◯ ◯ ◯ ◯

To Do

Activities

Time		

Notes

Twin Baby Log

Time	Feeding	Diaper	Medicine	Feeding	Diaper	Medicine

Tummy Time

	◯ ◯ ◯ ◯ ◯
	◯ ◯ ◯ ◯ ◯

To Do

Activities

Time		

Notes

Twin Baby Log

Time	Feeding	Diaper	Medicine	Feeding	Diaper	Medicine

Tummy Time
○ ○ ○ ○ ○
○ ○ ○ ○ ○

To Do

Activities		
Time		

Notes

Twin Baby Log

Time	Feeding	Diaper	Medicine	Feeding	Diaper	Medicine

Tummy Time

○ ○ ○ ○ ○
○ ○ ○ ○ ○

To Do

Activities

Time		

Notes

Twin Baby Log

Time	Feeding	Diaper	Medicine	Feeding	Diaper	Medicine

Tummy Time
○ ○ ○ ○ ○
○ ○ ○ ○ ○

To Do

Activities		
Time		

Notes

Twin Baby Log

Time	Feeding	Diaper	Medicine	Feeding	Diaper	Medicine

Tummy Time	
	◯◯◯◯◯
	◯◯◯◯◯

To Do

Activities		
Time		

Notes

Twin Baby Log

Time	Feeding	Diaper	Medicine	Feeding	Diaper	Medicine

Tummy Time	
	○ ○ ○ ○ ○
	○ ○ ○ ○ ○

To Do

Activities		
Time		

Notes

Twin Baby Log

Time	Feeding	Diaper	Medicine	Feeding	Diaper	Medicine

Tummy Time	
	◯ ◯ ◯ ◯ ◯
	◯ ◯ ◯ ◯ ◯

To Do

Activities

Time		

Notes

Twin Baby Log

Time	Feeding	Diaper	Medicine	Feeding	Diaper	Medicine

Tummy Time

	○ ○ ○ ○ ○
	○ ○ ○ ○ ○

To Do

Activities

Time		

Notes

Twin Baby Log

Time	Feeding	Diaper	Medicine	Feeding	Diaper	Medicine

Tummy Time

| | ○ ○ ○ ○ ○ |
| | ○ ○ ○ ○ ○ |

To Do

Activities

Time		

Notes

Twin Baby Log

Time	Feeding	Diaper	Medicine	Feeding	Diaper	Medicine

Tummy Time

	◯ ◯ ◯ ◯ ◯
	◯ ◯ ◯ ◯ ◯

To Do

Activities

Time		

Notes

Twin Baby Log

Time	Feeding	Diaper	Medicine	Feeding	Diaper	Medicine

Tummy Time	
	◯ ◯ ◯ ◯ ◯
	◯ ◯ ◯ ◯ ◯

To Do

Activities		
Time		

Notes

Twin Baby Log

Time	Feeding	Diaper	Medicine	Feeding	Diaper	Medicine

Tummy Time	To Do
○ ○ ○ ○ ○	
○ ○ ○ ○ ○	

Activities			Notes
Time			

Twin Baby Log

Time	Feeding	Diaper	Medicine	Feeding	Diaper	Medicine

Tummy Time

	◯ ◯ ◯ ◯ ◯
	◯ ◯ ◯ ◯ ◯

To Do

Activities

Time		

Notes

Twin Baby Log

Time	Feeding	Diaper	Medicine	Feeding	Diaper	Medicine

Tummy Time

	○ ○ ○ ○ ○
	○ ○ ○ ○ ○

To Do

Activities

Time		

Notes

Twin Baby Log

Time	Feeding	Diaper	Medicine	Feeding	Diaper	Medicine

Tummy Time
◯ ◯ ◯ ◯ ◯
◯ ◯ ◯ ◯ ◯

To Do

Activities

Time		

Notes

Twin Baby Log

Time	Feeding	Diaper	Medicine	Feeding	Diaper	Medicine

Tummy Time

	○ ○ ○ ○ ○
	○ ○ ○ ○ ○

To Do

Activities

Time		

Notes

Twin Baby Log

Time	Feeding	Diaper	Medicine	Feeding	Diaper	Medicine

Tummy Time

○ ○ ○ ○ ○
○ ○ ○ ○ ○

To Do

Activities

Time		

Notes

Twin Baby Log

Time	Feeding	Diaper	Medicine	Feeding	Diaper	Medicine

Tummy Time

	○ ○ ○ ○ ○
	○ ○ ○ ○ ○

To Do

Activities

Time		

Notes

Twin Baby Log

Time	Feeding	Diaper	Medicine	Feeding	Diaper	Medicine

Tummy Time

	○ ○ ○ ○ ○
	○ ○ ○ ○ ○

To Do

Activities

Time		

Notes

Twin Baby Log

Time	Feeding	Diaper	Medicine	Feeding	Diaper	Medicine

Tummy Time

	○ ○ ○ ○ ○
	○ ○ ○ ○ ○

To Do

Activities

Time		

Notes

Twin Baby Log

Time	Feeding	Diaper	Medicine	Feeding	Diaper	Medicine

Tummy Time

	◯ ◯ ◯ ◯ ◯
	◯ ◯ ◯ ◯ ◯

To Do

Activities

Time		

Notes

Twin Baby Log

Time	Feeding	Diaper	Medicine	Feeding	Diaper	Medicine

Tummy Time

	◯ ◯ ◯ ◯ ◯
	◯ ◯ ◯ ◯ ◯

To Do

Activities

Time		

Notes

Twin Baby Log

Time	Feeding	Diaper	Medicine	Feeding	Diaper	Medicine

Tummy Time

◯ ◯ ◯ ◯ ◯
◯ ◯ ◯ ◯ ◯

To Do

Activities

Time		

Notes

Twin Baby Log

Time	Feeding	Diaper	Medicine	Feeding	Diaper	Medicine

Tummy Time
○ ○ ○ ○ ○
○ ○ ○ ○ ○

To Do

Activities		
Time		

Notes

Twin Baby Log

Time	Feeding	Diaper	Medicine	Feeding	Diaper	Medicine

Tummy Time

	◯ ◯ ◯ ◯ ◯
	◯ ◯ ◯ ◯ ◯

To Do

Activities

Time		

Notes

Twin Baby Log

Time	Feeding	Diaper	Medicine	Feeding	Diaper	Medicine

Tummy Time

	◯ ◯ ◯ ◯ ◯
	◯ ◯ ◯ ◯ ◯

To Do

Activities

Time		

Notes

Twin Baby Log

Time	Feeding	Diaper	Medicine	Feeding	Diaper	Medicine

Tummy Time

○ ○ ○ ○ ○
○ ○ ○ ○ ○

To Do

Activities

Time		

Notes

Twin Baby Log

Time	Feeding	Diaper	Medicine	Feeding	Diaper	Medicine

Tummy Time

	◯ ◯ ◯ ◯ ◯
	◯ ◯ ◯ ◯ ◯

To Do

Activities

Time		

Notes

Twin Baby Log

Time	Feeding	Diaper	Medicine	Feeding	Diaper	Medicine

Tummy Time

	○ ○ ○ ○ ○
	○ ○ ○ ○ ○

To Do

Activities

Time		

Notes

Twin Baby Log

Time	Feeding	Diaper	Medicine	Feeding	Diaper	Medicine

Tummy Time	
	○ ○ ○ ○ ○
	○ ○ ○ ○ ○

To Do

Activities		
Time		

Notes

Twin Baby Log

Time	Feeding	Diaper	Medicine	Feeding	Diaper	Medicine

Tummy Time

	○ ○ ○ ○ ○
	○ ○ ○ ○ ○

To Do

Activities

Time		

Notes

Twin Baby Log

Time	Feeding	Diaper	Medicine	Feeding	Diaper	Medicine

Tummy Time

	○ ○ ○ ○ ○
	○ ○ ○ ○ ○

To Do

Activities

Time		

Notes

Twin Baby Log

Time	Feeding	Diaper	Medicine	Feeding	Diaper	Medicine

Tummy Time

◯ ◯ ◯ ◯ ◯
◯ ◯ ◯ ◯ ◯

To Do

Activities

Time		

Notes

Twin Baby Log

Time	Feeding	Diaper	Medicine	Feeding	Diaper	Medicine

Tummy Time

	○ ○ ○ ○ ○
	○ ○ ○ ○ ○

To Do

Activities

Time		

Notes

Twin Baby Log

Time	Feeding	Diaper	Medicine	Feeding	Diaper	Medicine

Tummy Time

	◯ ◯ ◯ ◯ ◯
	◯ ◯ ◯ ◯ ◯

To Do

Activities

Time		

Notes

Twin Baby Log

Time	Feeding	Diaper	Medicine	Feeding	Diaper	Medicine

Tummy Time

	◯	◯	◯	◯	◯
	◯	◯	◯	◯	◯

To Do

Activities

Time		

Notes

Twin Baby Log

Time	Feeding	Diaper	Medicine	Feeding	Diaper	Medicine

Tummy Time		To Do
	◯ ◯ ◯ ◯ ◯	
	◯ ◯ ◯ ◯ ◯	

Activities

Time		

Notes

Twin Baby Log

Time	Feeding	Diaper	Medicine	Feeding	Diaper	Medicine

Tummy Time

	○ ○ ○ ○ ○
	○ ○ ○ ○ ○

To Do

Activities

Time		

Notes

Twin Baby Log

Time		Feeding	Diaper	Medicine	Feeding	Diaper	Medicine

Tummy Time

○ ○ ○ ○ ○
○ ○ ○ ○ ○

To Do

Activities

Time		

Notes

DATE: _____

Twin Baby Log

Time	Feeding	Diaper	Medicine	Feeding	Diaper	Medicine

Tummy Time

	◯ ◯ ◯ ◯ ◯
	◯ ◯ ◯ ◯ ◯

To Do

Activities

Time		

Notes

Twin Baby Log

Time	Feeding	Diaper	Medicine	Feeding	Diaper	Medicine

Tummy Time

	○ ○ ○ ○ ○
	○ ○ ○ ○ ○

To Do

Activities

Time		

Notes

Made in the USA
Las Vegas, NV
07 July 2022